MISS FRANCES'
STORY BOOK
of
MANNERS
for the
very young

MISS FRANCES'
STORY BOOK
of
MANNERS
for the
very young

By DR. FRANCES R. HORWICH

Illustrations by Mina Gow

RAND McNALLY & COMPANY

NEW YORK • CHICAGO • SAN FRANCISCO

Message to Parents

Miss Frances' Storybook of Manners for the Very Young was written because so many parents have asked for guidance in how to acquaint their young children with good manners. The early years are a good time to start. What the child learns when he is very young, he remembers. This is especially true of manners because they become a basic part of his personality.

Therefore, manners, as practiced in our way of living, have been woven into a series of stories written especially for this book. Stories are a joyful way of learning. These stories can serve as examples of behavior. They can also stimulate many discussions between you and your children.

Greetings, farewells, parties, picnics, dining, introductions, and many other social situations in our daily living, all have their particular forms of social behavior. This Storybook of Manners for the Very Young introduces the child to many of these situations.

The correct use of such phrases as "Thank you," "I'm sorry," "May I," "Good morning," and "No, thank you," are included in the stories. What to do in church, when visiting, at the table, on a picnic, at a party, in a restaurant, and in the market, are also illustrated.

Some of the stories will serve as a reminder to the child as to what to do when others are resting; when he sneezes or coughs; and when someone presents him with a gift.

Of course, we must remember that manners and acceptable social customs are not learned overnight. Knowledge of them comes gradually. That is why I hope you will use this book as a reference book, sharing the stories with your children again and again. And I have included at the end a guide for using the book in this way.

As your child gradually understands and makes these manners a natural part of himself, he will become a more thoughtful person. Such thoughtfulness will bring him happiness in his relationships with his family and with his friends in the neighborhood and at school.

I hope that you and your children will enjoy this Storybook of Manners for the Very Young. I think you will.

Miss Frances

CONTENTS

MISS FRANCES'
STORY BOOK
of
MANNERS
for the
very young

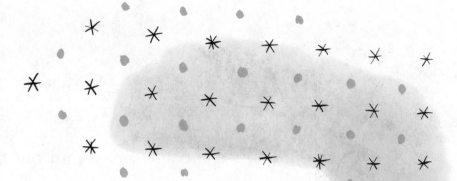

GOOD MORNING

"Good morning, Sally," Mother said with a smile as she walked over to close the bedroom window.

Sally opened her eyes very slowly, and then closed them again for just a second.

"It is morning and time to get up. Breakfast will be ready soon," continued her mother.

Sally was awake now and took a big stretch. All her mother could see were her head and her arms, because she was stretching her legs and toes under the covers.

"You didn't say good morning, Sally. What's the matter?" asked Mother. Still Sally didn't say a word.

Mother helped Sally climb down from her bed. Sally really didn't need any help

because she could get in and out of bed very easily. But it was fun sometimes to have Mother help.

As Sally was taking off her pajamas, she looked up at her mother with a big smile and said, "Good morning."

Now both Mother and Sally were laughing and feeling happy.

Boys and girls, do you know that saying "Good morning" helps make you feel happy? It helps you start your day off in a nice way. It helps make the other person feel good, too.

So, whenever you see someone for the first time in the morning, be sure to say "Good morning."

Let me tell you a secret—it is more fun if you smile when you say it!

You try it tomorrow morning.

EXCUSE ME

The doorbell rang. Timmy knew that meant Uncle John was there. He started to run toward the door. Suddenly there was a crash. Timmy had bumped into Sally's table, and all her doll dishes fell to the floor. Sally's doll party was all upset. Sally was very unhappy. Timmy was sorry, too.

Daddy opened the door and greeted Uncle John.

Mother went over to help Timmy and Sally. She put her arm around Timmy and asked: "What do you say to Sally?"

"Excuse me, Sally—I'm sorry. I didn't mean to knock them over. It was an accident."

Timmy and Mother then helped Sally pick up all the dishes and put them on the table again.

When they were finished, Mother, Timmy, and Sally went over to say hello to Uncle John.

When accidents happen, I hope you remember to say "Excuse me, I'm sorry," just as Timmy did.

AT THE TABLE

Daddy, Mother, Betty, and Ricky sat down at the dining-room table for dinner. The table looked so pretty, and they knew the food would taste good, too.

Before anyone started to eat, Ricky said grace. It was his turn. He said it in a soft voice, just loud enough so everyone at the table could hear every word.

Mealtime is a wonderful time. Everyone has something to share with the others. Betty told a story that she had heard in school. Daddy described a very fine red car he had seen down the street. And when it was Ricky's turn, he told about the garage that he and his friend Johnny had built with his blocks.

Mother's turn was last. She told them she had something new for them. It was something special that she had baked for dessert. She didn't tell them what it was, because she wanted it to be a surprise. She did say: "It is delicious, and I know that all of you will like it very much."

Because Mother wanted the dessert to be a happy surprise, no one tried to guess. They decided to finish all the food on their plates, and then they would be ready for dessert.

Sometimes, Ricky and Betty think it is very hard to wait for their turn to talk or tell a story at the table. It seems especially hard when they have something very nice that they want to share with the others.

But Ricky and Betty know that when Daddy is talking, everyone must listen. Then, when it is Betty's turn, Ricky, Mother, and Daddy listen. And while they listen, they eat their dinner.

Mother looked around and saw that Daddy, Betty, and Ricky were finished, so she knew it was time for dessert.

Betty helped Mother carry the dishes to the kitchen. Sometimes Ricky helped, too. But this time Daddy and Ricky planned what they were going to do together after dinner.

Suddenly it was very quiet. Betty came in and sat down in her place. Mother had asked her to come in, so she would not see the dessert out in the kitchen.

Then Mother came in, carrying the dessert. It looked delicious. There was whipped cream on top. There were little pieces of apple on the sides.

"What is it?" asked Ricky.

"Is it a cake?" asked Betty.

"I think it is a whipped-cream pie," said Daddy.

"No," said Mother. "It has a very interesting name. It has a girl's name. It is called 'Apple Brown Betty'."

Everyone looked surprised.

"It has your name," Ricky said, laughing, and pointed to Betty.

" 'Apple Brown Betty.' That is a fine name, and please, Mother, may I have a large serving?" said Daddy.

Mother took a big spoon and served the Apple Brown Betty.

"Mother, some day will you make a dessert called 'Daddy'?" asked Ricky.

BOBBY'S BIRTHDAY PARTY

Tomorrow is Bobby's birthday. He will be four years old. He will have a birthday party. Bobby and his mother will get everything ready for the party.

Four of Bobby's friends were invited to the birthday party. His mother called their mothers and asked if the children could come to the party. She told them to bring the children in the afternoon after their naps.

Early on the morning of Bobby's birthday his mother went to the kitchen to bake the birthday cake. What kind of cake should she bake? She thought and thought. Then she remembered that Bobby liked big, high cakes that were light and fluffy. So she decided to bake a big sunshine cake. That would be just right. The yolks of the eggs would make it gold color.

When the cake was baked, she showed it to Bobby. It was the biggest and highest

cake he had ever seen. He liked it so much that he jumped up and gave his mother a big hug.

"What color frosting would you like, Bobby?" she asked him.

"White frosting. I like white frosting best," answered Bobby.

Bobby watched his mother put the frosting on the cake. She spread it all around the cake with a special knife.

"Where did I put the candles?" asked his mother as she looked around the kitchen.

"Here they are. We need four, don't we?" Bobby picked up the candles and put them near the cake.

"You put them on, one at a time, where you want them," his mother suggested. "Be careful not to stick your finger into the frosting."

Bobby was very careful. When he finished, he counted the candles. "One, two, three, four." That was just right, because he was going to be four years old.

His mother handed him one more candle and said, "Put this one on for good luck, Bobby."

There were other things that Bobby and his mother had to do to get ready for the party.

Mother checked the games, to be sure they were ready.

She had a new record which she hid on a high shelf because she wanted that to be a surprise for Bobby. She knew all the children would enjoy it.

Then they looked for Bobby's favorite storybook which she would read to the children at the party.

They went to the freezer to make sure that the ice cream was there.

The paper napkins, hats, and spoons were on the cupboard shelf. Everything was ready.

Now it was time for Bobby to take his rest so he would enjoy his birthday party. That is very important, isn't it?

Later in the afternoon the doorbell rang. Bobby's friends were arriving for the party. Mary and Susan came first. Then came Jimmy and Don. Each child handed a package to Bobby. He was very happy and remembered to say "Thank you." Bobby liked his birthday presents very much.

Then he and his mother played with all the children. They played games on the rug and sofa. Soon they listened to the new record, and had fun marching and dancing to the music. When they were tired, all of them sat on the floor, even Bobby's mother. She read a good story from Bobby's favorite book. It was funny, and they laughed when they looked at the pictures.

Then it was ice-cream-and-birthday-cake time. Bobby invited his friends to the dining-room table. First, they put on their hats. Next, they tucked in their napkins. Then came the ice cream. It was pink and white and looked very good.

Bobby's mother brought in the cake, and put it in front of Bobby. The candles were lighted. Everyone sang "Happy Birthday" to Bobby. Then they told him to blow out the candles.

Bobby blew hard several times. The candles were all out.

Bobby's mother cut the cake and served it to the children.

"It's delicious!" they said as they ate it.

When they had finished eating their cake and ice cream, it was time for everyone to go home. The party was over.

The doorbell rang. There was Susan's mother. She had come to take Mary and Susan home. Just as they were getting ready

to leave, Jimmy's daddy rang the doorbell. "I came for two boys named Jimmy and Don," he called out in a gay voice.

Everyone was happy. Bobby thanked all of his friends for coming to his birthday party.

What do you think Don said to Bobby's mother?

"Good-by, I liked Bobby's party."

Don was very thoughtful, wasn't he?

CAPS OFF INDOORS

One Saturday morning Hugh and his daddy decided that they would go to visit their friend Mrs. Johnson. She lived quite far away, in a big white house with a white fence around the yard.

Hugh liked Mrs. Johnson because she always had a surprise for him.

It was a very cold day, so Hugh and his daddy had to wear their winter coats and caps.

As soon as they were ready, they climbed into the car which was parked in the driveway.

Daddy drove carefully, and Hugh sat up, big and tall, right beside him. Soon they were in front of Mrs. Johnson's house. Together they walked up to the door. Hugh

rang the bell. Mrs. Johnson opened the door and said:

"Good morning—please come in. I am so happy to see you."

Daddy took his cap off and shook hands with Mrs. Johnson.

Then Hugh and Mrs. Johnson shook hands. Daddy reached over and gently took Hugh's cap off.

"Why did you take my cap off?" asked Hugh.

Daddy put his hand on Hugh's shoulder and explained:

"Boys and men always take their caps and hats off when they enter a house or an apartment."

"Why, Daddy?"

"Because it is polite to take your cap off, Hugh. When you remember to take it off, that is one sign you are a big boy. Very small boys don't know that they should take their caps off indoors. But when boys are as big as you are, they try hard to remember. Isn't that right, Mrs. Johnson?"

"Yes, it is," she answered.

Mrs. Johnson then told them to put their coats and caps on a nearby chair.

"I have something very special to show you downstairs in the basement," she added.

Hugh and his daddy hurried to take off their wraps.

"There," said Hugh. "Now let's go."

Carefully they walked down the steps to the playroom in the basement. Mrs.

Johnson led them to the corner where there was a box.

"Look, Daddy," Hugh shouted with joy, "there are puppies in the box—real, live ones!" He was very happy.

Daddy was pleased, too.

Mrs. Johnson, Hugh, and Daddy sat down near the box. They watched the four little puppies for a long time.

"Oh, I'm glad we came," said Hugh.

"So am I," said Daddy, as he patted Hugh's shoulder.

SHARING WITH YOUR FRIENDS

It was raining outdoors, so Tommy and his friend Bill were playing inside with their toys. They had all of their blocks out on the living-room floor. They worked hard and built a beautiful garage with an upstairs and a downstairs place to park cars.

After a while Bill grew tired. He sat down and rested for a minute.

Then he looked over at Tommy. "I'm tired," he said. "May I look at one of your books?" He reached over toward the table where several of Tommy's books were lying.

"No! You can't have the book. It's mine!" screamed Tommy.

Tommy's mother was in the next room, and she heard his loud and unhappy voice. She came to the door and listened. This is what she heard Bill say:

"Tommy, I won't tear your book. I'll take good care of it."

Tommy came over to Bill, then, and said in a soft voice: "I'm sorry, Bill. You may look at my book, but be very careful."

Tommy's mother smiled, and went back into the other room.

MOTHER'S PARTY

Mother was spreading cheese on crackers. Nancy was wiping the glasses at the sink. Bobby was polishing the silver tray at the kitchen table. Everyone was busy getting ready for the party.

"How many guests are coming?" asked Nancy.

"Six—three men and three women," answered Mother.

"Then you will need eight glasses. Six for the guests, and two for you and Daddy. I have them all ready," said Nancy.

"You are a good helper. Now open your mouth," laughed her mother, and she poked a cracker with cheese into Nancy's mouth.

"Would you like one, Bobby?"

"One what?"

"A cracker with cheese. Here, open your mouth wide."

"Oh, that's good," Bobby said, as he swallowed the last little bit.

"Bobby has finished the silver tray, Nancy has finished the glasses, and I have finished putting cheese on the crackers. Dinner is cooking, and the table is all set. Now it is time for us to get cleaned up," said Mother as she hurried them out of the kitchen. "Daddy should be finished with his shower by now."

Upstairs they went. Quickly they got cleaned up and were all ready for the party.

One by one, they went back downstairs to the kitchen.

"Bobby, you look just right in your white shirt and blue pants." Daddy gave him a big pat on his shoulder.

"You have a white shirt and blue pants, too. Don't you, Daddy?"

"Nancy, your dress is so pretty, and I like the way you fixed your hair." Mother gave Nancy a little kiss right on the forehead.

"What is your job, Bobby?" asked Daddy.

"I have to pass the crackers first, and the nuts later."

"What will you do, Nancy?" Daddy asked.

"I will answer the doorbell, and later pass the napkins and plates."

"It all sounds fine to me. I am glad you and Mother planned it that way," said Daddy as he nodded his head.

Ding—dong! The doorbell rang.

33

"Hello, Mr. and Mrs. Smith," called Nancy.

While Mother and Daddy were greeting them, the doorbell rang again. This time it was Mr. and Mrs. Wells.

Bobby ran over to say hello to them.

Just then the doorbell rang another time, and Nancy hurried to open the door for the Parkers.

Now all the guests were there.

Mother called Nancy and Bobby to the kitchen, while Daddy invited all the others to sit down in the living room.

"Here, Nancy, you take this tray with the napkins and plates."

"Fine," said Nancy.

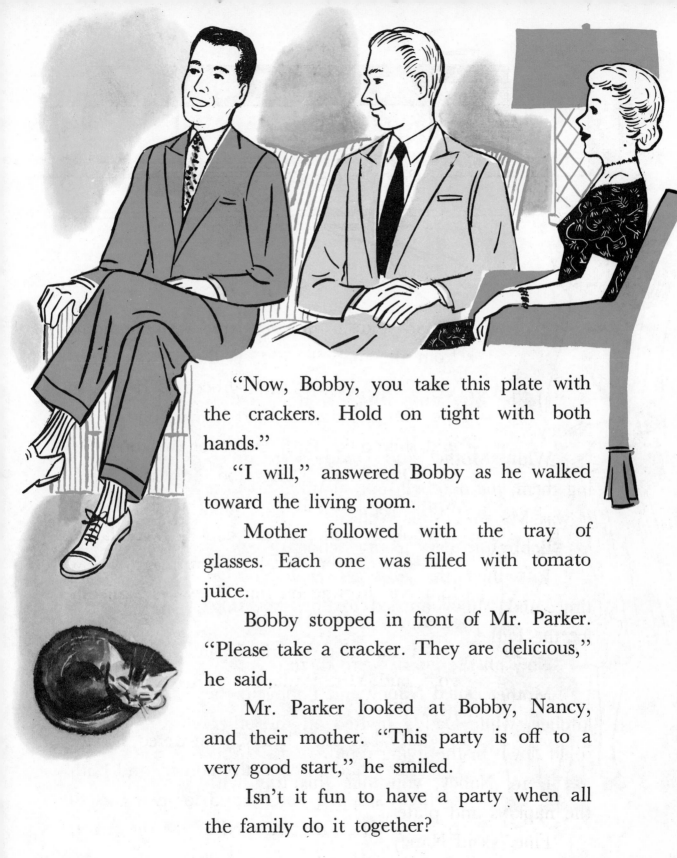

"Now, Bobby, you take this plate with the crackers. Hold on tight with both hands."

"I will," answered Bobby as he walked toward the living room.

Mother followed with the tray of glasses. Each one was filled with tomato juice.

Bobby stopped in front of Mr. Parker. "Please take a cracker. They are delicious," he said.

Mr. Parker looked at Bobby, Nancy, and their mother. "This party is off to a very good start," he smiled.

Isn't it fun to have a party when all the family do it together?

COOKIES

David and his mother were walking home from the market. Mrs. Williams was carrying a very large bag of groceries. It was so big that she had to hold it with both arms, and she could hardly see over the top of it.

David had a bag, too. It was a small white bag, and it was filled with all sorts of cookies. Some of the cookies were large, and others were small. There were a few that had frosting on top. They were all different shapes.

"I am glad we don't have very far to go," said Mrs. Williams. "This bag is very heavy."

"My bag isn't heavy," answered David.

They had reached the corner, and both of them stopped and waited for two cars to pass by. Then they hurried across the street.

"Hi, David!" called his friend, George, as he rode his tricycle to meet them. "Where have you been? I have been looking for you."

"Hello, George," David and his mother replied together.

Mrs. Williams pointed to her big bag of groceries. "You can guess where we have been, can't you?" she said.

"Yes, you guess, George, and then I will show you what I have in my bag," added David.

"You went to the market, didn't you?" George laughed as he said it, because he could tell that was where they had been.

Mrs. Williams walked on in front, and the boys came along slowly behind her. They stopped for a minute, so David could open his bag and show George what was in it.

George took a peek and said: "Oh, cookies—just what I like."

"Me, too," said David. "Let's eat them."

They were near their apartment door, and they could see David's mother go inside. When they were in front of the door, David sat down on the step. George climbed down from his tricycle and sat beside him.

The bag was open, and they took turns reaching in for a cooky. They took only one cooky at a time. They took very small bites, too. That way, the cookies lasted much longer.

When the cookies were all gone, George said: "Thank you for the cookies, David."

"You're welcome, George. I'm glad you liked them. Say, I'm thirsty. Let's go inside and get a drink of water," David suggested.

They opened the door and walked up the stairs together. David turned to George and said: "When you go to the store with your mother, and she buys some cookies, you will give me some of yours, too, won't you?"

"Of course I will," answered George.

And they walked happily to the kitchen to get their drinks of water.

PLEASE

"Mother, I'm hungry. Give me some crackers," called Michael, as he came through the door. He had a big smudge of dirt on his cheek. His hands were black from playing with his tricycle and wagon.

Again he called: "Mother, where are you? I'm hungry. I want some crackers."

"Here I am, Michael. I am in the bedroom," answered his mother. Her voice sounded cheerful, and Michael ran right into the bedroom.

He started to put his head in her lap.

"Wait a minute," his mother laughed. "You will wipe all of that dirt off on my dress. How about washing your face and hands?"

Looking up at his mother, Michael said in a loud voice this time: "Take the box of crackers down so I may have some."

"I didn't hear you say 'please'," his mother said softly as she walked with him toward the bathroom.

"Please," said Michael.

"That is much better. I will be happy to get the crackers for you. You get real

clean and then come to the kitchen. You
and I will have a party. Crackers and milk.
Doesn't that sound good?"

"Oh, boy! That sounds just right,"
Michael answered as he reached for the soap.

Do you remember to say please when
you ask your mother to give you some
crackers? I hope you do.

41

THE AUTO RIDE

Dick's daddy, Mr. Ross, walked down the steps of their house.

"Dick—Judy," he called in a loud voice. Both children, who were playing together, came running to him.

"I have an errand to do, and I wonder if you would like to go along for a ride," he asked.

"Oh, yes, good, let's go," they shouted and ran toward the car.

"Wait a minute, not so fast! Judy, you run home and ask your mother if you may come along. We will wait for you. Dick, I told Mother you were going with me."

As Judy ran across the lawn to her house next door, Mr. Ross put a small package on the front seat of the car. Then he opened the door and told Dick to sit on the back seat.

By this time they could see Judy running toward the car. She could go with them and was very happy.

"Careful, don't fall," cautioned Mr. Ross. "You climb into the back seat with Dick. Both of you sit down so that no one gets hurt."

Mr. Ross closed the door carefully and then climbed into the front seat and started the car. Off they went.

Soon they were out in the country, and there were so many things to see. There were cows, telephone poles, fences, horses, big trucks, barns, and silos.

Mr. Ross turned and drove up a narrow lane where he stopped the car.

"Hello, Mr. Brown," he called to the man who came over to the car. "Meet my boy Dick, and his friend Judy. They came along for the ride."

"Hello, Dick," said Mr. Brown, shaking his hand.

"Hello, Judy," and Mr. Brown shook her hand also.

Both children sat quietly while Mr. Ross and Mr. Brown talked. Then Mr. Brown took the small package and stepped back from the car.

All of them said good-by to one another, and Mr. Ross backed the car all the way to the main road.

Now they were on the way home. Dick and Judy could see all of the same things that they had seen before. It was fun looking for them.

They had been so busy looking out the window that they didn't know they were back home. The car stopped, and they were surprised when Mr. Ross opened the back door and said: "Climb out."

The children started off to play, when Mr. Ross said: "Judy, don't you think you should run home and tell your mother that we are back from our ride? It is almost suppertime."

Judy ran down the sidewalk and across the lawn to her house, while Dick and his daddy went into their house.

They could hear Judy singing while she ran. She was very happy.

Suddenly Judy stopped running. She remembered something. She turned around and ran back to Dick's house. The front door was closed, so she rang the bell.

Mr. Ross opened the door. When he saw Judy he laughed, and said: "Are you back already?"

"I forgot to say 'thank you' for the ride, so I came back to tell you. Now I must go home. Good-by."

"Good-by, Judy," called Mr. Ross. He closed the door and walked to the kitchen, where Dick and his mother were busy getting supper.

"Dick, do you know why Judy came back? She thanked me for taking her along for that nice ride. I didn't hear you say thank you. Did you forget?"

Dick reached up and quietly whispered, "Thank you," in his daddy's ear.

"You're welcome," his daddy answered. "It was a very good ride, wasn't it? You tell Mother all about it, while I finish some things in the other room."

A SURPRISE VISIT FROM GRANDMOTHER

Margaret was in the bathtub. She was supposed to be taking a bath, but she was really playing in the water. She had washed her face and hands and was waiting for her mother to come and help her finish with her bath.

Margaret heard the doorbell ring. She wondered who was there. She knew she couldn't climb out and run to the door because she was all wet. She could hear voices, but she couldn't quite figure out who was there.

Soon she heard footsteps. She knew that her mother was coming.

"Margaret, guess who is here!" called out her mother as she came to the tub to help Margaret finish with her bath.

"Nana is here," continued her mother. "Let's hurry and finish so that you can get dressed and run out to see her."

Margaret always called her grandmother "Nana."

Margaret could hardly sit still while her mother finished bathing her. She wanted to hurry and see her grandmother.

When Margaret stood up to get dry, she rubbed with one towel while her mother rubbed with another towel.

"There," her mother said. "We are finished. Hurry now and get dressed. Your clean clothes are on your chair in your room."

"You don't have to hurry. I see you." And there was Nana standing in the bathroom door. Margaret jumped right up into her arms. They hugged and kissed each other, while Mother stood there and watched them.

Then Margaret jumped down and ran into her bedroom to get dressed.

Nana and Mother came in to help Margaret. But she didn't need any help. She slipped right into her panties, shirt, slip, and dress. And, last, she put on her socks and shoes.

"There, I am all dressed." Margaret stood up big and tall.

"Come here, sweetheart. I have something for you," said Nana, opening her purse. She handed a very small box to Margaret. What could it be, thought Mother.

"Oh, thank you, Nana. I wonder what it is," cried Margaret. She sat down on the floor and carefully opened the box.

Look what she found! It was a clothespin doll that Nana had made just for her. It had a very pretty dress and bonnet.

Margaret was so happy that she jumped up from the floor and ran over and kissed Nana, first on one cheek and then on the other.

The doorbell rang. All three of them stood up, and then Margaret ran toward the hall.

This time Margaret knew it was her daddy because he always rang the bell a special way. First, it was a little short ring, and then a long one. She hurried and opened the door for him.

Margaret climbed up into her daddy's arms and gave him a big kiss and hug.

"Guess who is here, Daddy!"

"I don't know—who?"

"Nana surprised us, and look, she brought this clothespin doll for me."

"Wonderful," said Daddy and, carrying Margaret in his arms, he walked over and gave Mother and then Nana a big kiss, too.

IN THE MARKET

Mother was pushing her basket filled with groceries toward the cashier's counter. Nancy was walking slowly right behind her. There were so many good things to look at on the shelves that Nancy turned her head first one way and then the other.

A big, tall man in a white apron stopped his work and said: "Here, little girl, have a cooky."

"My name is Nancy, and I am a big girl," replied Nancy, standing close beside her mother.

"Oh, that is a nice name. Here, Nancy, have a cooky from this box."

Nancy looked up at her mother to see if she should take one. Her mother nodded her head, so Nancy carefully reached for the cooky. Then the man passed the box to Nancy's mother. She took one, too.

Can you guess what happened? Nancy and her mother said, "Thank you," at the same time.

"You are very welcome," the man answered.

While they were eating their cookies, they stood in line at the cashier's counter.

"He is a nice man, isn't he?" Nancy said to her mother.

"Yes, he is, Nancy."

MOTHER'S CHAIR

Dinner was ready on the table. Mother called Billy and his daddy, who were in the living room watching television. Mother called them just once, and they came hurrying to the dining room. Mother was standing behind her chair, waiting for them. Billy ran behind his chair, and Daddy stood behind his.

"Billy," said his daddy, "whose turn is it to pull out Mother's chair? Did you do it last night?"

"No, Daddy, you did it last night. It is my turn tonight," answered Billy, as he hurried around the table. He pulled his Mother's chair out slowly, and when she sat down he helped her push it closer to the table.

"Thank you, Billy," his mother said with a smile. "You and Daddy take such good care of me."

Daddy winked his eye at Billy and said: "It is fun to take good care of Mother."

Billy laughed and answered: "She takes care of us, so we take care of her."

Then they bowed their heads, while Daddy said the blessing.

ALICE, OUR BABY SITTER

"Alice will be here in a few minutes. I know you will have fun together tonight," Betty's mother said to her as she finished dressing. Betty's mother and daddy were going to a dinner party. Alice was coming to take care of Betty while they were away.

Betty liked to have Alice come to stay with her, when her mother and daddy went out in the evening. Alice always had many interesting stories to tell Betty and also games for them to play. Sometimes, she told her about the things boys and girls do in school. Other times, they played games together until it was time for Betty to go to bed. They were very special games. They played them while they sat on the sofa. Games like "Simon Says" and "You Guess What I See."

The doorbell rang. Daddy opened the door, and there stood Alice smiling and happy.

"Hello there," said Betty's daddy.

"Good evening," answered Alice.

While Alice was hanging up her coat, Betty came running in to see her.

"Hi, there," said Alice.

"Hi," said Betty.

Soon it was time for Betty's mother and daddy to leave. They had their coats on and came into the living room to say good-by to Betty and Alice.

"Betty, have fun with Alice and remember to go to bed when it is time. Good night, darling." Her mother leaned over and gave her a big kiss.

"Good-by now," called Daddy, as he started to open the door.

Betty and Alice waved to them from the living-room window. Then back to the sofa they went and played "Simon Says." They had lots of fun.

When it was bedtime, Alice said: "Can you guess what time it is?"

Betty guessed, and she was right, so together they went to the bedroom.

While Betty got ready for bed, Alice turned the covers back and fluffed the pillow.

It didn't take Betty long. She didn't forget any of the things she had to do to get ready for bed.

When she was in bed, Alice asked: "Now, which story do you want me to read? Here are three of your books, and you choose which one of these you want me to read."

Betty knew there was time for only one story. But it was very hard to choose. Finally, she decided that she wanted the story about the baby robins.

Alice sat on the edge of the bed. Betty stretched her arms and legs out straight. She nestled her head in the pillow. She was very comfortable.

Alice read the story in a soft voice. It was very quiet, and when Alice had finished reading the story, she whispered, "Good night, Betty."

"Good night, Alice."

Alice turned out the light and closed the door of the bedroom. While Betty slept, Alice went back to the living room. She sat on the sofa and read a book until Betty's daddy and mother returned from the party.

When they came home, Betty's mother asked: "Was everything all right, Alice?"

"Oh, yes, we had fun together, and Betty went to bed when it was time," Alice answered with a pleasant smile.

"Thank you very much, Alice. Here is the money you have earned for taking care of Betty. Now her daddy will take you home. Good night, Alice."

"Good night and thank you," said Alice as she went out the door.

CUTTING THE GRASS

Jim and his dad were out cutting the grass one Saturday morning. It was hot, because the sun was shining very bright. They were working very hard. Jim walked alongside his dad while he pushed the lawn mower. Whenever Jim saw a little twig or stick, he would pick it up and run over and put it into the basket.

They kept right at work until all the grass was cut. Then Dad said: "Jim, will you please carry the basket, and I will take the lawn mower."

"I will take it, Dad, and when we get in the house let's have something cool to drink. I'm hot."

"Yes, I am hot, too, and also tired. We will find something cool to drink and a cool place to sit and rest."

When they reached the back porch, together they put the lawn mower and basket away, and then went into the kitchen.

First, they washed their hands. Then, Jim got two glasses from the low shelf of the cupboard, while his dad took the bottle of milk from the refrigerator. He filled both glasses.

Jim and his dad then sat down at the kitchen table near the window and enjoyed the cold milk.

"Jim, thank you for helping me cut the grass. You were a big help. I like to have you help me with my work."

"Oh, I had fun, Dad. I hope the grass grows a whole lot, so we will have to cut it again soon."

THE CHOCOLATE SODA

Sue and her mother were downtown. It was a very warm day, and they were tired. They had finished all of their errands and shopping. Soon they would take the bus home.

"Sue, would you like a nice chocolate soda?" asked her mother.

"Oh, yes, Mother. Let's have a chocolate soda with straws." Sue was so happy she jumped up and down while she said it.

Sue took her mother's hand, and they walked down the street. Then they went through a big revolving door into a drugstore.

"See those two high stools at the counter? Let's go over there." Sue's mother helped her climb up and sit down. Then her mother sat down beside her on the next stool.

A man wearing a white jacket stood behind the counter and smiled at them. First, he put down a glass of water and a paper napkin for each of them. Then he asked: "What would you like today?"

In a soft but very happy voice Sue said: "A chocolate soda with straws, please."

Her mother added, "I would like a chocolate soda, too."

There were so many things to watch that Sue didn't know which way to look.

Another man behind the counter served a toasted sandwich to a woman who was sitting on the other side of Sue. That looked good, too.

Then Sue could see the man who was making their sodas. It was fun to watch him pull the handle of the faucet of soda water that made the bubbles in the glass.

Sue started to turn around to see what was on her other side, when her mother cautioned her not to slip off the stool. Then the man brought the two tall glasses. He put one in front of Sue, and the other in front of her mother.

"Thank you," said Sue.

"Thank you," said her mother.

"You are welcome, and I hope they taste very good," answered the man as he put the straws beside the glasses.

"Our sodas look delicious, don't they, Sue?" her mother said, as she helped Sue tuck the paper napkin into the neck of her dress.

Sue unwrapped the two long straws and put them into her glass. Then she had to sit up tall to take her first sip.

"This is good," said Sue.

"How do you like your soda?" asked the man behind the counter.

"We are enjoying them very much," answered Sue's mother.

Sue was busy drinking her soda so she couldn't talk. Then she took the spoon with the long handle and stirred her soda. Carefully, she took a spoon of ice cream. It was hard to get the ice cream up to her mouth without spilling any.

Sue and her mother were so busy eating

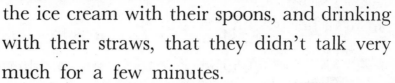

the ice cream with their spoons, and drinking with their straws, that they didn't talk very much for a few minutes.

Sue's mother finished her soda first. Then Sue could see that she had almost reached the bottom of her glass, too. So she put her lips to the straws and sipped the last little bit.

Sue looked up at her mother and said, "It's all gone."

"That was just right, wasn't it? Now what are you going to do with the paper napkin?" asked Mother.

Sue took the napkin from her neck and wiped her mouth. When she was finished, she put the napkin near her empty glass. Then she was ready and jumped down very carefully.

Together, Sue and her mother walked to the cashier and paid for their sodas.

"Good-by," called the man behind the counter.

Sue turned around and waved good-by to him.

They left the drugstore and walked to the corner for their bus.

BEING HELPFUL

"Henry, come and say good-by to Mrs. Parker," called his mother. "She is going home now."

Henry came running from the other room where he had been playing with his train.

"Good-by, Henry. It was nice to see you again," said Mrs. Parker.

"Good-by," answered Henry.

As Mrs. Parker was putting on her gloves, one fell to the floor. She started to pick it up when Henry's mother said: "Henry will pick it up for you."

Henry picked up the glove and handed it to Mrs. Parker.

"Thank you, Henry. That was very helpful of you to pick up my glove."

"You're welcome. Good-by again." And Henry ran back to the other room to play with his train.

Putting her hand on the doorknob, Mrs. Parker said: "Henry is a very helpful little boy."

"Yes, he is," answered Henry's mother. "He likes to be helpful."

THE "THANK YOU" PICTURE

Victor received a Christmas gift from his Aunt Marion. It was a very gay toy monkey. He was brown and had a long tail that curled at the end.

Victor was very happy with his present. He played with the monkey many different times during the day. He gave him a ride in his truck. He also carried him on his shoulder. And when the monkey got tired, he let him rest on the sofa.

Later in the day Victor decided to name the monkey. He thought and thought. Finally, he went into the kitchen and asked his mother: "Do you think 'Ginger' is a good name for my monkey?"

"I think that is a fine name," she answered. "Hi, Ginger!" she then called out to the monkey, as she gave him a pat on the head. This made Victor laugh. He did the very same thing. He patted him on the head and said, "Hi, Ginger!"

Victor started to leave the kitchen, when his mother called him back and asked: "Victor, you like your new monkey, don't you?"

"Yes, I like him very much," Victor answered, looking up at her.

"Don't you think it would be nice to tell Aunt Marion how much you like him? She would like to know that you named him Ginger. I have an idea," said his mother, as she walked over to him.

"You make a picture of Ginger for Aunt Marion, and we will put it into an envelope and mail it to her. She will like that."

"That is a good idea," said Victor, and he ran off to get his crayons and paper.

Victor sat down at his table and made a picture of Ginger sitting on the sofa. When he was finished, he showed it to his mother. She wrote "Ginger" at the bottom of the picture so that Aunt Marion would know that Victor had given the monkey a name.

Then Mother turned the paper over, and on the other side she wrote this little letter:

Dear Aunt Marion:

Thank you for sending the monkey. I love him. I named him Ginger.

Love,

Victor

She read the letter to Victor, and he took the pencil and put a little mark near his name.

"What is that?" asked his mother.

"That is a kiss for Aunt Marion," he said.

"Wonderful! Now you fold the paper so it will fit inside this envelope."

Victor folded the paper very carefully. Then he slipped it into the envelope and sealed it. Mother took her pen and wrote Aunt Marion's name and address on the envelope.

"Now we need a stamp," she said. "I will

get one and you may put it on the envelope."
She handed the stamp to Victor. He put it
in the corner.

"Now, when we go down the street, you
may put this letter into the mailbox."

That made Victor happy.

"Victor, do you know what this very
special letter is called?"

"No," answered Victor.

"It is a 'thank you' picture just for Aunt
Marion. When anyone gives you a present,
you want to be sure and say, 'Thank you.'
You know that, don't you?"

"Sure," said Victor.

"Aunt Marion lives far away, and therefore you couldn't say, 'Thank you' so instead
you made a 'thank you' picture for her."

"That was fun," said Victor. He took
Ginger and went off to play.

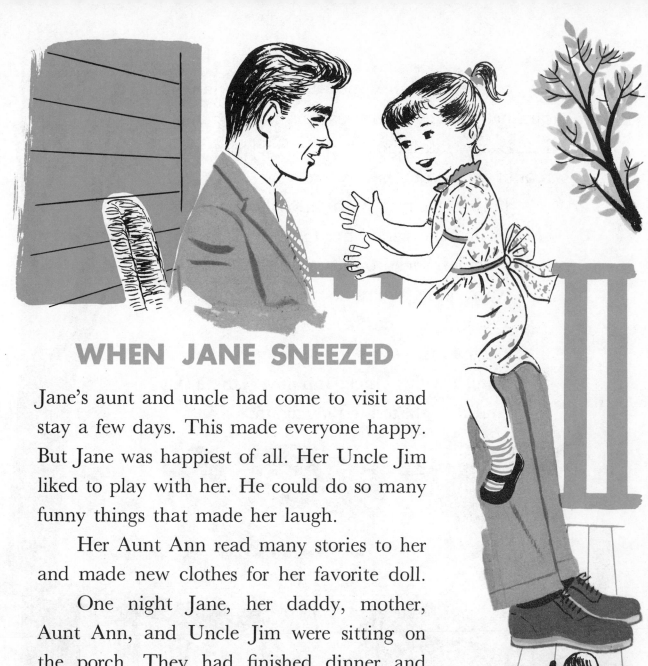

WHEN JANE SNEEZED

Jane's aunt and uncle had come to visit and stay a few days. This made everyone happy. But Jane was happiest of all. Her Uncle Jim liked to play with her. He could do so many funny things that made her laugh.

Her Aunt Ann read many stories to her and made new clothes for her favorite doll.

One night Jane, her daddy, mother, Aunt Ann, and Uncle Jim were sitting on the porch. They had finished dinner and were resting and visiting.

Jane was sitting on Uncle Jim's knee. Every now and then he would give his knee a little shake, and Jane would wiggle back and forth. Then both of them would laugh. They were really having a happy time.

Suddenly Jane sneezed. "Oh, Jane," said her mother, "here, use my handkerchief. I am sorry you forgot to cover your nose and mouth with your hands."

Jane blew real hard into the handkerchief. Then she wiped her face and gave the handkerchief back to her mother.

"Now, Jane, what do you say to Uncle Jim?" asked her mother.

"Excuse me, Uncle Jim."

"Sure, I will." Uncle Jim gave Jane a big hug, and they started to play again.

PLEASE MEET MY SON, HARRY

Harry and his daddy, Mr. Hurd, had a wonderful time looking at many different things in the big department store on Church Street. They had been having such fun that they forgot what time it was.

Suddenly, Mr. Hurd looked up at the clock on the wall.

"Harry!" he said. "We have to hurry. Mother will be waiting for us."

Harry didn't want to leave the store. There were too many things to see. But he knew he had to go with his daddy, so he took his hand. They hurried out of the store.

"Hello there, Mr. Hurd," called a big, tall man.

"Well, hello to you, Mr. Jackson. How nice it is to see you this morning. Mr. Jackson, please meet my son, Harry," Mr. Hurd said proudly.

Mr. Jackson shook hands with Harry and said: "I am very happy to meet you, Harry. You are a fine, big boy."

Harry looked up and answered: "Thank you."

"Mr. Jackson, Harry and I have been having a wonderful time in the store. We are late and have to hurry to meet Mother. It was lots of fun seeing you. Hope we get together soon for a real visit," said Harry's daddy.

"I understand," answered Mr. Jackson with a big smile. "You run along. Good-by to both of you."

"Good-by," said Harry.

"Good-by, Mr. Jackson," said Mr. Hurd.

Then Harry and his daddy hurried to find Mother.

ON THE STREETCAR

Timmy and Michael were going to their grandmother's house. Both of them were sitting in one seat on the streetcar. Their mother and daddy were in the seat behind them. Everyone was looking out the window because there were many things to see.

The streetcar stopped, and some people got off and other people got on. Michael watched them give their money to the man who was standing at the end of the car.

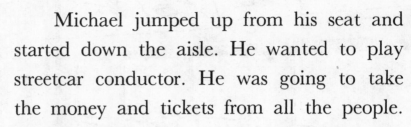

Michael jumped up from his seat and started down the aisle. He wanted to play streetcar conductor. He was going to take the money and tickets from all the people.

Michael's daddy went after him and brought him back to his seat. He lifted Michael up on his lap and explained: "You can't play streetcar on a real streetcar because you will disturb the other people. You see how they need all the space to walk and to get off or on the car."

Michael listened, while he looked around the car. He really wanted to play streetcar because he thought it would be fun.

"You and Timmy can play streetcar when you get to Grandmother's house. Now why don't you ask Timmy if you may have the seat by the window."

Just then the man at the end of the car called out, "Lincoln Street!"

"That's the street where we get off," said Mother. She pulled the cord so the car would stop, and all of them walked down the aisle toward the door. When the car stopped, they climbed down and walked to the sidewalk.

As the streetcar began to move, Michael called out: "Good-by, streetcar."

LUNCH IS READY

"Lunch is ready," called Mother.

Everyone came running to the table. Mother took one look at Gretchen and walked over to her, saying quietly: "Gretchen, you forgot to wash your hands and face."

Gretchen didn't want to go then and wash herself because she was afraid she would miss out on some fun.

"I am sorry, Gretchen, but you cannot sit down to lunch with dirty hands and face," her mother explained. "Hurry and get washed so that we can start. If you hurry, we will wait for you."

Gretchen decided she would hurry and ran off to the bathroom. Mother, Daddy, Susan, Mary, and Jim sat down in their regular places. Then they waited for Gretchen to come.

It didn't take her very long. She had washed her hands and face with soap and water. She looked so clean and happy. She climbed into her chair.

"Now, we are all ready. Daddy, please serve the lunch," said Mother as she winked her eye and smiled at Gretchen.

SH! DADDY IS SLEEPING

Larry opened the door and called in a big, loud voice: "Mother, Mother, may I go to the store with Henry?"

His mother came quickly and quietly, putting her finger to her mouth.

"*Sh!*" she whispered, "Daddy is sleeping. Let's not wake him."

"Why is he sleeping now?" asked Larry. "It's not night."

"Daddy is very tired, so he is taking an extra rest. See, he is over there on the sofa. Now, what do you want to do?"

"Henry is going to the drugstore to buy something for his mother. I want to go with him. May I go, Mother?"

"Yes, you may go, but you must remember to be very careful when you cross the street. Look both ways. Thank you for coming in and asking me. Have a good time."

Larry hurried out the door. His mother closed the door quietly so the noise wouldn't wake Daddy.

IN CHURCH

"Betty Lou, would you like to go to church with Mother, Bob, and me today?" her daddy asked her when they were sitting at the breakfast table on Sunday morning.

"You have to be very quiet in church," added Bob.

"Not when you sing," said Betty Lou, "and I am good at singing."

"That's right—you sing very well. Bob, did you know that I taught Betty Lou the words to one of our hymns yesterday?" Mother explained. "She can sing all of it."

"Oh, that is fine," said Daddy. "Then I hope you will go to church with us today."

"I will," said Betty Lou.

Breakfast was over, and everyone went to get dressed for church.

Daddy was ready first. He sat down in the living room and read the paper while waiting for the others.

Next came Bob. He had on his best blue suit and white shirt. He sat down on the hassock and looked at the funny paper.

Soon Mother and Betty Lou came to the living room. "Look at us. We are ready," cried Betty Lou.

When they were in the car driving toward the church, Mother asked Betty Lou and Bob if they would try hard to sit still and listen in church. Both of them promised they would try hard.

When they reached the church, Daddy parked the car. They met many of their friends and said "Good morning" to each one of them.

Betty Lou and Bob sat very quietly through the church service. When it was time to sing, they joined in. Betty liked the organ music, too.

When church was over, they said good-by to everyone and walked back to their car.

As Daddy unlocked the car, he turned to Betty Lou and Bob and said: "I am very proud of both of you. You were very good."

THE PICNIC

Everyone was having a wonderful time at the picnic. Daddy played ball with the children. Mother took them for a walk to see the flowers and trees. They also played other games together.

When it was lunchtime, Mother rang the bell.

"Are we all here?" asked Daddy.

"I hope so," answered Mother. "Let's count and see.

"Sally, Mary, Dick, Daddy, and me. All five of us are here," Mother called out. "Now everybody find a place to sit. The food is all ready."

Each one looked around the picnic table and found a comfortable seat. Mother served the food.

When all the plates were served, they started to eat.

"I'm hungry, and this looks good," said Dick.

"It tastes good, too. This fried chicken is delicious, Mother," Daddy said, as he smiled and winked his eye.

"Thank you, Daddy," answered Mother. "I am glad you like it."

"The potato salad is good, too," added Sally.

Dick and Daddy asked for second helpings, and they ate every bite.

Then Mother served strawberry shortcake for dessert.

After they were finished eating, Sally and Mary helped Mother put all the empty containers into the picnic basket. Daddy and Dick carried the other things back to the car.

When all the things were packed, Daddy said: "Now, everyone look around and make sure that we have picked up everything."

"Yes, let's be sure that we are leaving the picnic grounds just as nice and clean as they were when we came," said Mother.

Dick ran over and picked up a paper napkin that had fallen under the table.

"That's fine. Now let's go home. Did everyone have a good time?" asked Daddy as they walked toward the car. They all nodded their heads and said "yes" at the same time.

DO YOU KNOW THE ANSWER?

I think you know the answer to this question: When does a boy take off his cap or hat?

There are many different times when a boy does this, aren't there? Let's think of a few times.

1. When he is eating lunch? Yes.
2. When he is playing outdoors? He doesn't need to take it off unless he wants to.
3. When he visits in his friend's home? Yes.

4. When he rides in an elevator in a store or other building? Yes, it is polite for him to take off his cap or hat if a lady is present.

5. When he rides in a streetcar or bus? No, he does not need to take his cap off then.

Here we had only five different times. Now, you think of other questions about when a boy takes his cap off.

Did you think of some? Ask your daddy or mother to tell you the answers.

PLEASE, DADDY

Stanley and his mother and daddy were having lunch in a restaurant. After they told the waitress what they wanted to eat, Stanley looked at his daddy and said: "Please, Daddy, may I show you something now?"

"Yes, Stanley, what is it?"

Together Daddy and Stanley walked to the front of the restaurant. Stanley showed Daddy a little box filled with different kinds of candy. It was a very pretty bright-red box. The candies were wrapped in gold and silver paper.

"It is very pretty, Stanley," said Daddy. "They have so many different boxes of candy here, don't they?"

"I like the red one best," said Stanley, pointing to it in the big glass case.

"Now we must go back to our table. We don't want to leave Mother alone too long.

And our lunch will be coming soon." Daddy took Stanley's hand, and they walked back to their table.

Stanley and his daddy told Mother all about the red box of candy. While they were talking, the waitress brought their lunch.

First she served Mother's toasted sandwich. Then she served Stanley the sliced-chicken sandwich he had ordered. Last she gave Daddy his sandwich. Mother had iced tea in a tall glass, Stanley had milk, and Daddy had a cup of hot coffee.

All of them enjoyed their lunch very much. Just as they were finishing, Stanley said: "Please, Daddy, buy that red box of candy for me."

"Not this time," Daddy answered.

"But I said 'please,' Daddy. That means you should buy it for me," insisted Stanley.

"I know you said 'please,' Stanley, and I am glad that you did. But sometimes even when we say 'please,' we cannot have the things we want. This is one of those times," explained Daddy.

"That's right," added Mother. "It is time for us to be on our way. Stanley, would you like to go with Daddy to pay for our lunch?"

Stanley jumped down from his chair. He and Daddy went to the cashier's desk. Mother waited for them near the door.

MOLLIE'S WASHCLOTH

Mollie was washing herself so she would be ready when her mother called her for dinner. She had washed her face and neck. Now she was scrubbing her elbows.

She took her towel and rubbed her arms until they were dry.

Carefully she hung her towel back on the rack. She folded it, neat and straight.

Then she pulled the plug and let the water go down the drain.

Mollie started from the bathroom when she thought of something and went back to the wash basin.

Can you guess what she had forgotten to do?

She had left her wet washcloth all wrinkled in a ball on the edge of the basin.

Mollie wrung her cloth dry and then hung it beside her towel.

You know where to hang your washcloth, don't you?

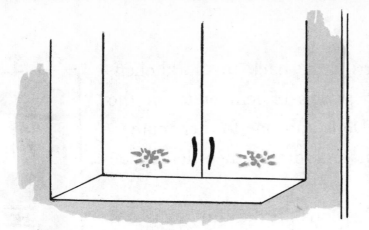

CLOSE THE DOOR QUIETLY

Slam! The kitchen screen door closed with a bang. Mother looked up. Doris was walking toward her mother. She looked hot and tired.

"What's the matter, Doris?" asked her mother, as she stooped down and took Doris' hand.

"I'm tired and thirsty," said Doris.

"Yes, you look tired and hot. I will fix a glass of lemonade for you. Would you like that?" asked her mother.

Doris nodded her head. She knew that lemonade would be cool and it would taste good, too.

"You go wash your hands and face. By the time you finish, the lemonade will be ready."

Doris went to the bathroom. Mother got busy making the lemonade.

When Doris came back to the kitchen, there were two glasses of lemonade on the table. One for Doris and one for her mother. They sat down and drank their lemonade very slowly.

Mother told Doris all the things she did while Doris was outdoors playing.

She baked a cake. She washed and dried the dishes. She made her grocery list, and she also made the beds.

Then Doris told her mother all the things she did outdoors. She played with Helen until her mother called her. She rode her tricycle and then played in the sandbox.

When Doris had finished telling her mother about all these things, both of their glasses were empty.

"Now, do you feel rested and cooler?" asked Mother.

"Yes—I am going outdoors again," said Doris, as she slid off her chair.

"Wait a minute. I want to tell you something before you go."

Doris came around to her mother's chair.

"When you came in, you were hot and tired and you forgot and slammed the door.

Now you are rested and cool, so I know you will remember to close the door quietly. Run along and have a good time." Her mother smiled and stood up.

Doris went out and closed the screen door very quietly. She peeked back at her mother and waved to her.

"Thank you, that was very quiet," said her mother, as she waved to Doris. Then she went back to her work.

WAIT FOR YOUR TURN, CATHY

Cathy and her daddy were standing on the corner, waiting for the bus. They were going downtown because Daddy was taking Cathy to the dentist.

It was very cold, and Cathy wished the bus would hurry and come. She kept looking for it. There were some women and children standing near them. They were also waiting for the bus.

"Here it comes," called out one of the boys who was standing near the curb.

Cathy and her daddy looked and that was right—the bus was coming. Everyone stood back and waited for the big bus to stop.

The door opened, and a man and a little boy carefully climbed down. When they walked away, the people started to climb up into the bus. Cathy wanted to be first and started to push the boy in front of her.

"Careful, Cathy, no pushing. We have to wait our turn," her daddy reminded her. Cathy stepped back and waited.

The people in front of them climbed up into the bus, one by one. Then it was Cathy's turn. She took a big step. Then she held on to the long rail and climbed up the second step. Her daddy was right behind her. Quickly, she pulled off her mitten and gave some money to the bus driver. She had the money to pay for her daddy. Cathy was a little girl, so she didn't need to pay for her bus ride.

"Thank you," said the bus driver.

"You're welcome," called Cathy as she walked down the aisle, looking for a seat where she and her daddy could sit together. She found one. Cathy took a seat near the window, and her daddy sat down beside her.

They enjoyed their ride downtown.

LADIES FIRST

Marilyn and Joe were in the elevator with their mother and daddy. Joe was watching the girl who pressed the floor buttons and also pulled the handle that made the elevator go and stop.

When the elevator stopped, the doors opened and the girl said: "First floor."

Joe stepped aside and stood beside his daddy. His mother and Marilyn walked out first. Then Daddy and Joe walked out. Joe said good-by to the girl in the elevator.

Daddy said: "Good for you, Joe. You remembered that ladies go first. I am glad that you waited with me while Mother and Marilyn walked out." Daddy gave Joe a friendly pat on the shoulder and added: "You are getting to be a big boy. I am proud of you."

Mother winked her eye and smiled at Joe. This made him very happy, too.

OPEN THE DOOR, PLEASE

Mother and Daddy had been shopping at the market. Dick and Josey stayed home. Josey played the piano and Dick sang. Sometimes they sang together. They were having a very good time when they heard someone call: "Open the door, please." They listened again because they were not sure who was calling.

"It's Mother!" said Dick, and he ran to the door. There stood Mother with two very large bags filled with groceries. They were so heavy and big that she just couldn't open the door by herself.

Dick opened the door and Mother walked in. She handed one bag of groceries to Josey, and they walked together toward the kitchen.

Mother called to Dick, "Daddy has more bags of groceries, so you stay there and open the door for him."

Dick started back toward the door, and there stood Daddy calling: "Open the door, please." He also had two bags of groceries, one in each arm.

Dick opened the door all the way so that Daddy could get through. Then Daddy said: "Thank you, Dick. I couldn't have made it without your help." He handed Dick one of the bags, and together they also walked to the kitchen.

"Look at all of the groceries you bought!" exclaimed Josey.

"Well, we are a big family and we get hungry—don't we?" her daddy replied, turning toward Mother.

"We certainly do," agreed Mother. "All of these groceries will last only a few days, and then we will have to go to the market again."

"Then I will have to open the door again, won't I?" asked Dick.

"Yes, you will, Dick."

A DRINK OF WATER

Jay was watching a television program in the living room. His mother, daddy, and sister Susan were also in the room.

Suddenly Jay got up from his chair and started toward the kitchen. He was thirsty and wanted a drink of water.

When he had taken only a few steps, Jay turned around and went back into the living room. He decided to ask the others in the room whether they also were thirsty.

"Mother," he asked, "would you like a glass of water?"

"No, thank you," she smiled. He then asked Daddy: "Would you like a glass of water?"

"Yes, Jay," Daddy answered. "I would like one very much."

"How about you, Susan? Are you thirsty, too?"

"No, Jay, I am not. Thank you for asking me."

Jay hurried out to the kitchen. First he took a drink of water for himself. Then he filled a glass for his daddy. He carried the glass of water very carefully with both hands.

"Here, Daddy. This is just for you." Jay handed the glass slowly to his daddy.

"Thank you, Jay. Now you sit down and enjoy your television program. I will take the empty glass back to the kitchen."

"All right, Daddy," Jay said, as he sat down in his chair.

WE SAY THANK YOU

1. When someone hands us something.
2. When someone holds the door open for us.
3. When someone does an errand for us.
4. When we receive presents.
5. When someone passes food to us at the table.
6. When someone helps us fix something.
7. When someone buys something for us.
8. When someone gives us a special treat.

There are other times when we say "thank you." Can you think of some?

IN THE RESTAURANT

Penny, John, and Bennet and their mother and daddy went into the restaurant. They were going to have dinner. When they were inside, a lady met them and asked Daddy "How many?"

"Five," answered Daddy.

"What does that mean?" asked Penny.

"There are five of us, so we need a table that is set with five places," explained Daddy.

"How do you know?" Penny asked again.

"Count how many of us there are," Daddy told her.

Penny counted: "One, two, three, four, five."

"See, Penny," her daddy said. "We need a table with five places. Then each of us will have his own chair and place at the table, just as we have at home."

Just then the same lady came back and asked them to follow her. Mother went first, and Penny, John, and Bennet followed. Daddy was last.

Mother showed the children where to sit. All were happy. There were menus at each place. Everyone looked at the menu because it told all the different kinds of food they could have. Mother read the menu to Penny so that she would be able to decide for herself what she wanted to have. Penny was too young to read a menu.

Soon a waitress came to their table and filled their glasses with water. She put a basket of rolls on the table, too. Then she took a small pad and pencil and wrote down the different foods that each one wanted. When she had all their different choices, she went to the kitchen to get the food.

Penny looked around the room. There were many tables. John looked around, too. "Look, every table is filled," he called out.

"Remember to use a small voice, John," his mother cautioned. "We don't want to disturb the other folks."

"May I have a roll?" asked Bennet.

"Help yourself and pass them around," Daddy suggested.

There were many different things to see, but Penny decided to eat her roll first. She broke the roll in half, and then she put some butter on it. Before she had finished eating it, the waitress brought her tomato juice. Penny, Mother, and Bennet had tomato juice. John and Daddy had grapefruit juice.

When they had all finished their juice, the same waitress brought their dinner. Everything tasted so good that they kept right on eating. They talked very little.

Soon it was dessert time. The waitress again handed each of them a menu. This time Daddy read the names of the different desserts to Penny so that she, too, could decide for herself which dessert she wanted.

"It's fun to eat in a restaurant once in a while," Mother remarked. "Then everyone can have something different if he wants it."

Everyone was busy deciding what he wanted for dessert.

"What will you have?" asked the waitress.

"Chocolate cake," answered Bennet.

"Strawberry ice cream," said John.

"Chocolate ice cream for me," called out Penny.

"Cherry pie," said Mother.

"Watermelon," said Daddy.

John laughed and said, "Everyone is having something different."

"I hope they are all good." Bennet laughed, too.

"They will be," said Mother.

The waitress brought the desserts, and she put the right one in front of each person.

When everyone had finished, Daddy left some money on the table for the waitress.

Then they all stood up and pushed their chairs under the table. Daddy walked to the cashier's desk and paid for the dinner. Mother and the others waited near the door for him.

When they were outside, Daddy asked: "Did everyone enjoy his dinner?"

"Yes, it was very good," they all answered.

"What else should we say to Daddy?" asked Mother.

"Thank you, Daddy," all said at once.

DO YOU NEED A TISSUE?

Margot, Bill, and Jack were playing grocery store on the living-room rug. Mother was at her desk writing.

Margot sneezed. Her mother immediately asked: "Do you need a tissue, Margot?"

But Margot was so busy playing that she didn't hear her mother.

Mother looked over at Margot. Then she walked over and handed a tissue to her, saying: "Here, Margot, please use this tissue."

Still Margot continued to play with Bill and Jack.

Mother stooped down near Margot and asked her to please stop playing for a minute. Margot did, and Mother handed her the tissue. This time Margot used the tissue and then started to hand it back to her mother.

Mother didn't take it. She said: "Listen, Margot, when you sneeze, or your nose runs, please use a tissue. Then, when you are finished with it, put it into the wastebasket. You can remember that, can't you?"

"Of course," replied Margot. She went at once to the wastebasket and dropped the tissue into it. Then she hurried back to Bill and Jack.

I'M SORRY

Ted was five years old. He was playing on the floor near his mother's chair. He had built a high hill with his wooden blocks and a piece of cardboard. Now he was ready to push his small truck up the hill. He pushed it carefully and slowly all the way up to the top. When the car reached the top of the hill, Ted took his hand away. The car slipped all the way back down the hill very fast. It was going so fast that when it reached the bottom of the hill, it kept on going and didn't stop until it hit Ted's mother's foot.

"Ouch!" she cried. "What hit me?"

"It was my truck. It slipped away from me," said Ted, as he came over to his mother.

"Here, I will rub it for you. That will make it feel better."

"Yes, that will help," said his mother. "Ted, when you bump or hurt someone accidentally, what do you say?"

"I'm sorry," answered Ted, looking up at his mother. "Yes, I am really sorry. Let me kiss you."

Ted gave his mother a big kiss and then ran back to his block hill.

THE LAST PANCAKE

Barbara, Mother, Daddy, and Uncle Oscar were enjoying breakfast together. It was Saturday morning, and they were having a good time visiting while they were eating.

It was a very special breakfast because Uncle Oscar was visiting them. Also, it was special because Mother had made pancakes.

Barbara, Mother, Daddy, and Uncle Oscar liked pancakes very much. Sometimes they had jelly or honey with them. But this Saturday morning they had pancakes and sirup.

Mother made the pancakes. She made a big plate of them. First she served Uncle Oscar's plate, then Daddy's plate, and then she put three small pancakes on Barbara's plate. Now that she had served everyone else, Mother also helped herself to some pancakes.

They were such delicious pancakes that everyone asked for more. This made Mother very happy. She liked to see everyone enjoy her pancakes.

Barbara looked around and said, "There is one pancake left. May I have it, Mother?"

"Why don't you share it with your Uncle Oscar and Daddy?" suggested Mother.

"Uncle Oscar, would you like some of this last pancake?"

"No, thank you, Barbara. I can't eat another bite," said Uncle Oscar.

"Daddy, would you like some of this last pancake?"

"Barbara, I have eaten too many pancakes already. I just can't eat any more," sighed Daddy.

Barbara looked at her mother.

"Barbara, you may have the last pancake. But it was polite to offer to share it with the others, wasn't it? Now you enjoy it." Mother smiled at Barbara as she passed the sirup to her.

TASTE IT

"Grandma, everything looks so pretty, and I know it will taste delicious," Mother said, as they gathered around the table.

It was Daddy's birthday, and Grandma was having a very special birthday dinner for him. Mother and Daddy and Nelga were there. Uncle Bill and Aunt Barbara were there, too. And, of course, Grandma and Grandpa.

There were place cards, so everyone knew where he was to sit. All of the men held the chairs for the ladies. Daddy held Nelga's chair and then pushed it in so she would be comfortable.

In the center of the table there was a beautiful glass bowl filled with flowers.

And at every place there was a lovely fruit cup. It had many different kinds of fruit. Nelga watched and waited until she saw her grandma start to eat the fruit. Then she knew that she could start eating, too.

"This fruit cup is very good," Aunt Barbara said.

"It certainly is," added Mother.

"Thank you," Grandma responded. "I am glad you like it."

When everyone had finished his fruit cup, Grandma served the main course. Everything smelled so good that Nelga could hardly wait.

There was a big platter of fried chicken. A silver bowl was filled with mashed potatoes. And another dish contained a green vegetable. Nelga could not see what kind of vegetable it was.

She waited quietly while the plates were being served. When her mother put the plate in front of Nelga, she looked at it closely.

There was the fried chicken, all white meat. That was the kind Nelga liked best. There were mashed potatoes with good brown gravy over them. And there were three pieces of asparagus.

Nelga picked up her fork and started to eat her chicken and potatoes. She enjoyed eating them very much.

"Mother, I don't want any of that." Nelga pointed to the asparagus and looked up at her mother as she said it.

"Nelga, do you know the name of that vegetable?" asked her mother.

"No, what is it?" asked Nelga.

"It is called asparagus," Mother said. "I like it very much, and I want you to taste it."

Nelga looked at her mother and then at her plate. She looked at everyone at the table. They were all busy eating, visiting, and laughing.

"Taste it," her mother said quietly, so that only Nelga could hear her.

Slowly, Nelga took her fork and lifted up a small piece of asparagus. She looked surprised and pleased as she ate it because it really tasted good.

Nelga hurried and finished her chicken, potatoes, and asparagus. When Grandma was ready to serve the dessert, Nelga was all ready.

First Grandma served a dish of ice cream to everyone. And then she brought in the birthday cake with all the candles lighted. She put it down in front of Daddy.

"It is a beautiful cake, Daddy," called Nelga.

"Yes it is," Daddy said. "And Grandma baked it."

Everyone sang the "Happy Birthday" song to Daddy. Then he blew out all the candles. After that Daddy took the candles off the cake and carefully cut the first piece.

Grandma helped Daddy cut and serve the rest of the cake.

Nelga tasted it. "This cake is delicious, isn't it, Daddy?" she asked, as she leaned over and looked at him.

Everyone at the table answered all at once: "It certainly is good."

Then Nelga smiled up at her mother and said: "Mother, you didn't have to ask me to taste this birthday cake."

Mother put her hand on Nelga's shoulder and said: "No, I didn't. And I know something else. The next time we have asparagus, I won't have to ask you to taste that, either, because you know how delicious it is."

Nelga smiled and went on happily eating her cake and ice cream.

IT'S TIME TO SAY GOOD-NIGHT

Daddy was reading the newspaper. John was playing with his train. He was eight years old and was allowed to stay up until eight o'clock. Mary Ann was sewing. She was twelve years and could stay up even later than John.

"Betty, it is time for you to go to bed," said Mother, as she came over to the table where Betty was playing with a puzzle.

"Not yet," said Betty.

"Oh, yes," said Mother. "It is time for you to go to bed. It is seven o'clock and that is your bedtime—remember?"

Betty remembered that she went to bed first. But she didn't want to stop playing with her puzzle. Mother helped her finish putting it together.

"Now you are ready, so say good-night to everyone," whispered her mother.

Betty crawled up on her daddy's knee and kissed him good-night.

"Good-night, dear. Sleep well," said Daddy, and he gave her a big hug and kiss.

Then Betty got down on the floor and said good-night to John.

"Good-night, Betty, and thank you for not stepping on my train." John liked Betty very much.

And last she said good-night to Mary Ann.

"Now I'm ready," said Betty, and she and Mother went to the bedroom.

"Tonight you may have other pajamas, so you look in your drawer and find the ones you would like to wear," her mother said, as she took the bedspread off and folded it carefully.

Betty hurried off to the bathroom. When she came back, she was all ready for bed. She kicked off her slippers. One went too far, and Betty ran over and picked it up. Then she put both slippers together beside her bed so they would be there when she woke up in the morning.

Mother reminded Betty to say her prayers.

Then her mother tucked her in and kissed her good-night. "You are a wonderful little girl, and I love you very much," said her mother.

"I love you, too," said Betty.

Mother opened the window and fixed the window shade. Then she turned out the light.

"Good-night again, sweetheart," called Mother, as she left the room.

Guide for Parents in Using This Book

This informal index will help you in selecting the manners story which will meet most closely the specific needs of your child.

Morning manners, 11-12

Napkins, 60-63
Naps, 22
"No, thank you," 101-02
Noisiness. *See* Voices, loud; Voices, pleasant
Nose wiping, 69-70, 109-10

Ownership, recognition of, 29-30

Parties, manners at, 19-24, 31-35, 116-22.
   Also see Birthday parties
Passing food, 31-35, 51, 103, 106, 113-15
Permission, asking, 42, 50, 78
Personal appearance. *See* Appearance,
   personal
Picking things up, 82-84
Playing together, 29-30, 98-100
Pleasantness, 12, 64, 94-96
Please, 35, 40-41, 71-72, 87-89, 98-100
Prayer, 15, 53, 125
Presents. *See* Gifts
Public conveyances, manners in: buses,
   85-86, 94-96; elevators, 85-86, 97; street-
   cars, 73-75
Public places, manners in: church, 79-81;
   picnic grounds, 82-84; restaurants, 60-63,
   87-89, 104-08; stores, 50-51; streetcars,
   buses, elevators, 73-75, 85-86, 94-96, 97
Pushing, 94-96
Putting things away, 58-59, 84

Quiet: when others are sleeping, 78; while
   adults are talking, 44; in church, 79-81;
   with doors, 91-93

Refreshments and treats, 58-59, 60-63,
   91-93, 103
Reporting back, 44
Requests, quick response to, 47-48, 55, 70,
   71, 76-77, 84, 91-93, 98-100, 109-10,
   113-15, 118-19
Restaurants, 60-63, 87-89, 104-08

Selfishness. *See* Generosity; Sharing
Serving food, 31-35, 113-15
Shaking hands, 43-44, 71-72
Sharing, 15, 29-30, 36-39, 113-15
Smiling, 12
Sneezing, 69-70, 109-10
Soap, use of. *See* Cleanliness
Speaking, manners when. *See* Voices, pleas-
   ant; Conversation, polite; the courtesy
   phrases, "Please," "Thank you," "May
   I," etc.
Streetcars, 73-75

Table manners, 15-18, 22-23, 52-53, 60-63,
   76-77, 85-86, 103, 104-08, 113-15, 116-22
Taking turns, 15-16
Talking, manners when. *See* Voices, pleas-
   ant; Voices, loud; the courtesy phrases,
   "Please," "Thank you," "May I," etc.
"Thank you," 22, 24, 39, 45, 48, 51, 59,
   62, 64, 65-68, 72, 83, 99, 101-02, 103, 108
Thank-you note, 65-68
Thank-you picture, 65-68
Thoughtfulness, 24, 52-53, 78, 98-100,
   101-02, 113-15
Tissues, use of, 109-10
Towels and washcloths, care of, 90
Traveling, behavior when, 73-75, 94-96
Treats. *See* Refreshments
Turns, taking and waiting, 15-16, 94-96

Unselfishness. *See* Generosity; Sharing
Unusual foods, 116-22

Visiting friends, 25-28, 42-44, 85-86
Voices, loud, 29-30, 40-41, 78, 105
Voices, pleasant, 15, 29-30, 105

Washcloths, care of, 90
Washing. *See* Cleanliness

"You're welcome," 39, 45, 51, 62, 64

Printed in U.S.A.